Story & Illustrations by:
Aliah Banchik © 05/30/2017

D ETERMINED

UN **Y** IELDING

VER **S** ATILE

INTE **L** IGENT

POW **E** RFUL

E **X** CEPTIONAL

I NNOVATIVE

C REATIVE

Contents

PREFACE

This book is no ordinary book. This book is yours to create. Learn about dyslexia and what it feels like having it through pictures and stories. If you prefer art over reading (like I do) then do not fear! This book is for you! Each illustration is intentionally void of color so that you can create the characters you like to see and watch them evolve! Make sure you have some markers nearby when reading this because it is your job to color the characters and give them life! Make it your own! Have fun :)

Chapter 1

68. That's a nice looking number. It's simple, makes sense, and it's even. Pretty nice right? Well, I gotta say it doesn't look that nice when it's circled at the top of your most recent math test.

As you can probably tell, math isn't my favorite thing. Well school kind of isn't my favorite thing. The academic part at least.

You see, I'm in 6th grade now and I have a love/hate relationship with school.

What I like:

- Art: Painting, drawing, sculpting, you name it, and I love it. I have a very active imagination and doing art is fun for me because I can just get creative for 40 minutes a day.

- Playing sports: Recess and gym are two of my favorite times of the day because I get to just run and play. During recess you can find me on the field playing flag-football with my guy friends or on the monkey bars at the playground doing flips. I am one of the fastest runners in my grade so people know to think twice before challenging me to a race.

For these reasons, I love school and look forward to going to it every day. But there are also some things that I don't like about school.

What I don't like:

- Math: Although I like the idea of math, in the sense that it's similar to a puzzle, I am not good at it. I get the wrong answers a lot of the time because I'm "sloppy" with my work. For example, I may copy down a problem incorrectly or something and then answer the one I wrote instead of the actual problem and then all my work is correct, but my answer is wrong. I just make a lot of silly mistakes and get things wrong which makes me not like math.

- Reading: I am a really slow reader and I don't like reading out loud because I always mess up. It is super embarrassing and makes me not want to participate in class. I really don't like it.

- Spelling: I wish this wasn't a class. It seems like 40 minutes just set aside for me to continually get things wrong one after another. What I have learned from this class is that the English language does not make sense and that sound-spelling is a myth.

Aside from those things, I do like school. I love Science and creative writing and all my friends make coming to school worthwhile.

Although I don't love the classes listed above, I still work hard to do my best. I mean, that's all you can hope for, right?

Chapter 2

My first class of today is Math.
Yay :/

I sat down and pulled out my math binder covered in doodles and stickers.

I doodle on all my binders. It just makes each subject look like fun and inviting even if in reality it really isn't.

My teacher, Ms. Jackson, asked us to start going over last night's homework with our neighbor so I pull out mine and started checking it over with my friend Sam.

We started off by reading our answers one by one. He would say one and I would say the next and after I had read a few, I told Sam to just read out his answers and I would say something if I had a different answer.

But the truth is, I had already gotten two wrong and just didn't want to keep saying I got a different answer. It's embarrassing. Plus I knew his were probably right so why waste time saying what I got?

A few minutes later Ms. Jackson finally says "Ok class. Now that we have partner-checked

homework, let's move on to the
warm up" and writes a warm-up
problem on the board.

"$6 + 3 = ?$"

I copied it down and began to work. I
am usually pretty good at simple stuff
like this. I don't mind problems like
this one because it's kind of like a
puzzle and I am good at solving
puzzles.

A minute or two passed and I had finished. I looked up to see my classmates still working away and felt a sense of pride that I was one of the first to finish. With my extra time, I checked over my work to make sure I had the right answer.

For once, I felt really confident it was right. In fact, I knew it couldn't be wrong since I had checked it so many times. Ms.

Jackson suddenly says "Ok class, who has an answer for me?" and my hand shot straight into the air.

Ms. Jackson called on me and I said with confidence "I got 12" and waited for her to write it on the board.

Except she didn't. In fact, she kind of froze and looked at me like my skin was blue or something. I was sitting there in my seat looking back at her waiting for her to say something when she finally said

"Uhh...Sorry Allie, that is incorrect".

I was shocked. I knew it was the right answer! I looked down at my paper like 3 times to double check and got the same answer every time, it had to be right! I then looked down at my paper and saw that my paper suddenly said "9 + 3" instead of "6 + 3".

There it was. My "sloppy" work.

Chapter 3

I was so embarrassed and sunk down into my chair as my classmates all shouted the correct answer to the problem: 9.

It felt like I knew what everyone was thinking. "Wow she can't even add? What's wrong with her?"

All these thoughts just rushing through my mind. I just wanted to crawl under the table and stay there forever instead of being stared at by all my classmates who got it right.

How can I feel motivated to try hard in school when I keep getting things wrong no matter how hard I try. My friends are all having fun and getting stuff right all the time and I'm just sitting there waiting for class to end to go play outside. It stinks. And the thing is, it's not just math.

Reading was my next class. The only thing this class was good for was for forcing me to come up with different tactics to avoid participating. For example when Mr. Silver would say "Allie (AL-LEE) would you like to read a passage?" I would respond with a variety of hand motions that say "I really would love to but I lost

my voice and can't read out loud"
(not).

That's always a good one until I
raise my hand a bit later and ask to
go to the bathroom and they say "Oh
great! Your voice is back! So when
you get back from the bathroom you
can be the first to read."

In all seriousness though, I get

really nervous and scared to read in front of the class. I am a solid 10 times slower at reading than most kids in my class and I almost always stutter on words. It's really embarrassing.

Every time I read it feels as though the room becomes so silent you could hear a feather land on the floor. In Africa.

There has got to be some reason why I feel the way I do and why I make the mistakes I make. I think I'll ask my mom what she thinks.

Chapter 4

When I got home from school that day I went straight to her room.

Backpack and shoes still on. I was determined to understand what was going on.

"Honey!" exclaimed my mom as she pulled me into her arms for a nice minute-long hug.

"How was school, Chickie-Chick?!"

Side note: something you should know about my mom is that she has a never ending list of nicknames that she calls me.

Sometimes it seems like she just comes up with them in the moment and expects me to respond to them so I basically respond to everything at this point. Monster, Cookie, Chicken, Princess, Lovie, Chicken-Pot-Pie, Angel-Face, Chick-e-dee........and the list literally never stops. So, if you see something that looks out of place anywhere in here, it's probably my mom creating a new nickname for me. Just a fair warning.

"School was eh. I got a 68% on my math test again and reading was not so great"

"Aw Chicken-Monster-Mash, I'm sorry to hear that. What can I do to help my little Chickpea?"

"Well I was gonna ask you about that. Do you think there's

something wrong with me?" and I
stumbled on the word "wrong".

"Well my little Flapjack, why don't
we bring you to the doctor and we
can let him take some tests for you
to see if there is something we can
do, okay?"

"Okay"

Chapter 5

That week leading up to the doctor's appointment I was really nervous. I had never thought that I might actually be different from any of my friends. I mean when we hang out it's totally normal and we always have a good time. The only place where I feel different is in the classroom.

The day was finally here and it was time for my appointment. My

mom and I walked in, sat down,
and she picked up some paperwork
from the front desk to fill out
while we waited.

It felt like an hour just sitting there
watching my mom scribble in pen
all over a beautiful white sheet of
paper polluted with dark, black
words. Then finally a nurse

popped out and said "Allie?" and guided me into a room.

About 10 minutes after my mom and I were placed in this room, a short older man with grey hair and a short grey beard walked in and said "Hello! I'm Doctor Avi

(AW-VEE). You're Allie?"

"Yep. That's me"

"So what brings you in here today, Allie?"

"Well, it's probably nothing I have just been doing poorly in math and reading and my spelling is kind of awful. But like I said, it's probably nothing. I'm probably just bad at those subjects. I don't even like them that much."

"Hmm. That is actually interesting Allie... What do you mean when you say you're 'bad' at them?"
"Well in math I've been told that I am really 'sloppy' with my work

because I always write equations down wrong for example and I just always get things wrong.

Always. In reading I'm just really slow and...well...bad at it."

He then turned to face my mom and asked "is it alright if we run a few tests?"

And meanwhile I'm just sitting there thinking "tests...math...68...I'd rather not...please say no"

but my mom answered before I could say anything.

"Yes of course. Let's get to the bottom of this" and we were guided into another room.

Little did I know that we would be in this room for a little over 4 hours just doing tests. I had a written assessment, a vocabulary test, reading comprehension questions, and I had to read out loud for a while on top of it all. When it finally ended I asked Doctor Avi, "So am I ok? What is the problem?"

To which he replied "I will let you know in about two weeks!"

:|

CHAPTER 6

These next two weeks couldn't have been worse. I was

hyper-aware of all of the mistakes I was making in my classes, and just felt really alone. I also couldn't stop thinking about what it would mean if there was something wrong with me. I would be different than everyone else.

I really didn't like that idea and it
made me feel like there was a pit in
my stomach all the time. But the
question I kept coming back to
when I spaced out in class was did I
want the tests to come back clear?
Did I want them to say that I am
perfectly fine? Or did I want the
tests to show something? I couldn't
decide.

Finally the two weeks of waiting were over and an answer was soon to come. Whether I liked it or not. My mom and I walked back to Doctor Avi's office and sat in the waiting room until he called us in. The waiting room was still just as old and boring as it was two weeks ago.

We walked into the same room we were placed in last time and to my delight Doctor Avi met us there quicker than he did last time. Only an 8 minute wait!

"So Allie, remember those tests you took? A few weeks ago" he asked as if he was talking to my 8 year old brother.

"I do"

"Well the results of the tests came back."

"Yes and?"

"Well I think I found an answer." Oh my gosh just get to the point already! It's not like you're announcing the next president for crying out loud! "Well Allie...you have Dyslexia"

Ugh...finally he said it! But I
suddenly wish he hadn't.

"Dyslexia? What does that mean?"

"Well you know how you mentioned
that you were having trouble with
math, reading and spelling to name a
few?"

"Yeah"

"Well the reason why is because
you have dyslexia. Dyslexia

means that your brain works differently than other people's and it makes reading, spelling, and math more difficult for you which is why you feel the way you do about your classes."

I just sat there staring at the floor.

Well, there was my answer. There was something wrong with me. I don't know how I felt about that. Should I be glad that I know that there is a reason why I am not doing well at school? Or should I be upset knowing that there is something wrong with me that sets me apart from my friends.

My mom and I walked back home and she was telling me how it's going to be fine and that having dyslexia won't change anything since I've always had it. I just didn't want to listen to her right then. I felt like I was walking around with a nametag that said "dyslexic". It was awful.

All I could think about was that yesterday I was fine. No dyslexia. No real problem. Suddenly I have dyslexia. A real problem.

CHAPTER 7

When I got home, I ran straight to my room, locked the door and just cried. I cried because I didn't know what else to do.

I didn't sleep well that night. I couldn't stop thinking. Thinking about me, about myself and my new problem. I had dyslexia. Me. Allie. I always had it and now I always will. Great. What were my friends going to think? Was I going to tell them? If I did, how would I tell them and would they like me less? I didn't know if I would ever fall asleep that night but somehow, in my never ending stream of consciousness

(con-shus-ness), I did.

The next morning when I woke up for school I was different. My mom woke me up so I was physically awake, but I had no desire to get out of my bed. At all. I just wanted to stay in bed and be dyslexic instead of going to school to be dyslexic. But that wasn't an option.

"Sunshine! Let's get going come on come on!"

Shouted my overly-peppy mom as she baked me my favorite breakfast: Mini chocolate chip pancakes with a side of...well...chocolate chips. (What do you want? I like my chocolate.)

"Boobaluhhh!! These pancakes are getting icey cold! Come out!" I'm not gonna lie. This woman knows me too well. The fresh scent of freshly baked pancakes with the gooey, melting, chocolate chips layered throughout, was indeed the only thing that could have gotten me out of bed that day. So props to you Mom for knowing how to get me up.

A little less than half awake, I slowly emerged from the warmth of my bed, slightly tripped on a shoe, banged into a couple of walls and then proceeded to miss the chair as I tried to sit, and landed on my butt. It was that kind of a day.

Once I had successfully gotten my butt in the chair, I started scarfing down my pancakes and within 2 minutes, all 7 were gone. Even though my tummy was now happy, I still was not. But school was still school, so I had to go.

Chapter 8

To kick off my first glorious day of being dyslexic, I had Math class first. I said hi to all my friends as we sat down at our desks. I decided I wasn't going to tell them and that I would just pretend nothing had changed even though everything had changed.

Once again I pulled out my pretty little math binder and lay it on the desk when all of a sudden, I hear a giggling. It sounded like it was directly next to me but I saw no one. I looked all around in every direction and still saw no one, yet the giggling was still there. And the weirdest part was that it sounded exactly like my laugh which freaked me out even more. Then as I looked to my left the weirdest thing imaginable happened. I saw me!

But it wasn't me. It couldn't have been me for I was sitting in my chair and most certainly not standing in front of myself, but she looked just like me. Just standing there, laughing. I looked around at all of my classmates to see if anyone else saw two me's and no one else seemed to see her. It was almost as if she was invisible to everyone except for me.

I just sat there amazed for a bit unable to say anything. Then through her giggles she said "Hey Allie".

Chapter 9

Shocked by the image of myself standing in front of me, I gasped and asked the other me "What are you? Are you real?"

"I'm Lexi! And of course I'm real. You see me, don't you? hehe" I nodded yes then asked "But why can't everyone else see and hear you"

"Well because I am a part of you, not them. You see, my full name is

Dyslexia. But you can call me Lexi for short. I heard my name yesterday at the Doctor's office and wanted to formally introduce myself to you! So hi!"

"So you are a real person but only I can see you?"

"Well technically I am inside your head so I am not a real person. I am only here for you!"

"So what do you do? Why are you here now?"

"Well you looked pretty sad and I am here to help so I wanna cheer you up! That's why I have been playing with your math hehe"

HEHEHE HE!!

"Wait wait. What? You made me get that wrong?"

"Well technically you didn't get it wrong cuz you got the right answer for the equation 9 + 3"

"But the equation was 6 + 3!" "Yeah but I changed the numbers on your page before you started working

so you would have to answer $9 + 3$
heheh"

"So then are you the reason my
numbers always get switched like
that?"

"Hehehe yeah! Isn't it funny?"
"No Lexi! It's embarrassing!
Because of you doing that I am
not doing well in math!!"

"Oh...I'm sorry Allie. I just wanted to make you to laugh. I thought it was funny"

"It isn't funny Lexi.

"I'm sorry. Why don't we go to the playground and cheer you up there!" "Lexi I can't I have class! You'll have to wait for gym or recess later. For now, just let me focus and stop messing up my math!" "Ok ok I'm sorry. I'll go back into your head and I'll try to stop."

"Thank you" and Lexi disappeared.

Ms. Jackson then turned around and shushed me and told me to do the next problem.

Chapter 10

Now we were onto multiplication. We were practicing times tables that we were supposed to be memorizing for homework. Ms. Jackson handed out a sheet of multiplication problems. "Alright" said Ms. Jackson. "We are going to do a little speed round. When I say 'go', answer as many problems as you can until I say stop. Ready? GO!" and I looked down at my paper and saw 4 X 8.

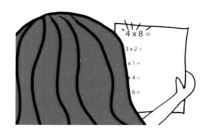

I sat there for a second trying to remember the answer that I had memorized the night before for homework. I knew I knew the answer but for some reason it wasn't coming to me. That's when I realized. It was Lexi.

While she was inside my head, she erased all the times tables I had memorized last night from my memory so I did not know any of the answers.

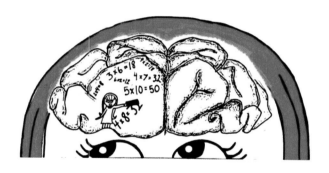

"Ta-dah!" exclaimed Lexi.

"Lexi! What are you doing?!" I yelled back.

"Ahh I'm sorry Allie!! Your brain just looked so cluttered with all that math so I wanted to make it look cleaner and prettier!"

"So you erased it?! Lexi I needed that math"

"Oh...I didn't know that. I'm sorry Allie"

Ms. Jackson turned to the class and said "Aaand stop! Pencils down"

I looked down at my paper and saw that I hadn't answered anything. Not a single question.

"Raise your hand if you answered 4 or more" said Ms. Jackson.

More than half the class raised their hands.

"Now raise your hand if you got 3 or more" and the rest of the class raised their hands. I was the only one with my hand down and Ms. Jackson noticed that. She then asked "How about you Allie?

How many did you get? Any number is a good number!" she said probably expecting me to say 1 or 2.

"Uhh...zero" and I felt everyone's eyes on me. She was not expecting that.

"Oh...uh no worries Allie. Just try a little harder while studying your times tables next time and make sure to do the homework!"

But the truth was I did do my homework and I always do my homework. It is just because of

Lexi that she thinks I am lazy and not working hard enough.

Chapter 11

That class was really frustrating. Every time I told Lexi to not do one thing, she would then do another thing that was equally as annoying. I kind of felt bad though because she wasn't trying to do any harm. In fact, I think she was trying to help me but everything she did was just kind of annoying and actually not helpful at all.

My next subject was now Reading with Ms. Slav. As she walked into the room and handed out books to everyone, Lexi ran over and stood right over my shoulder.

"What's that?" asked Lexi.

"It's the book we are reading today"

"Ohhh yuck"

I giggled and said to her, "I feel the same way."

Since Doctor Avi told me that dyslexia was the reason I was doing poorly in math, reading and spelling, I knew that that meant that Lexi was going to try to "help" me in this class too.

For the entire class, we just went around the room, everyone reading a passage of this book about a mouse. The first time it was my turn to read, I started

reading at a nice pace when all of
the sudden Lexi taps me.

I shrugged her off because I was in
the middle of a sentence and kept
reading. Then all of a sudden I
started reading slower. Well, not
unusually slow for me but it was
my normal speed which is
unusually slow to most. Tripping

and stuttering on a few words here
and there like good ole times.

I read, "One day when Mr. Wentz
saw Brendon walking on his block,
he asked to borrow his mawn
lower..." and my class started
laughing.

See, I didn't actually recognize
this mistake until my friend Elias

jokingly asked "Can I borrow your mawn lower?"

It was so embarrassing and it always happened to me. I turned to Lexi and asked "What did you do Lexi?"

"Not much! I just slowed you down because you were reading too fast and I couldn't understand the story. I also saw that they spelled 'mawn lower' wrong so I changed it for you" "Lexi they spelled it right. The word is 'lawn mower'" I said with a sigh.

"Whhaaatt?? I didn't know that!"
"Yes Lexi, now let me get back to class" and I followed along reading as one of my friends read out loud.

When it came around to be my turn again I started reading and I was on a roll. I was saying the words right, I was reading at a good pace, and I even sounded out a few big words. When I was done, I realized I didn't make any mistakes! I had a flawless read for basically the first time ever. But when the next person started reading the passage below mine, I was so lost. When did Brendon kill Mr. Wentz's dog?? How did Brendon become a mouse?? I couldn't remember a single thing I had read. It was like I didn't read it at all.

Lexi successfully refrained from "helping" with my pace and with the spelling of words on the page but she definitely did something else because I literally could not explain a single thing that happened in the passage I read. "Lexi..."

"Yeah Allie?"

"What was that...? Why can't I remember what I just read?" "Hmm I don't quite know why you don't rem- ooooohhh" she remembered. "I put your brain on an autopilot of sorts to help you read smoother. Maybe that turned off something else so you weren't comprehending what you read..."

It did kind of work for her intended purpose so I wasn't that mad, but it still backfired which was really annoying.

Chapter 12

Reading was finally over and I now had gym. Gym rocks. I love trying new sports. We just started our dodge ball unit with Mrs.

Ward which is one of my favorites so I am extra excited.

Mrs. Ward blew her whistle and yells "Alright! Give me 5 laps!" and we all start running.

Lexi was the first to run and I had to catch up to her. Maybe I get my speed from her? Who knows. This is all so weird.

"I am SO excited!! I love dodgeball!"
"Lexi, no offense but maybe it would be better if you didn't try to help me with this. I am pretty

good at sports by myself and don't really need help"

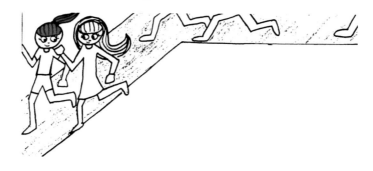

"Just trust me Allie"

Well I might as well give her a chance. Plus, if she runs around enough maybe it would tire her out enough that she won't want to "help" me with my homework when we get home.

Mrs. Ward blew her whistle and we all stopped running and lined up in two teams on either side of the dodge balls. Lexi was running in place right beside me waiting for the whistle to sound.

"On your marks, get set...go!"

And Lexi and I bolted towards the balls. We were the first to get there.

I immediately grabbed one and threw it at the first person I saw and hit him square in the shoulder. "Here take this", said Lexi as she handed me a ball.

I took it and ran back to the base line and located my next target. As

I released the ball to throw, I hear
Lexi shout "Allie! Look out!" and as I
turned I saw a ball heading straight
towards my face.

"Well...it's been nice knowing you
world" I thought to myself as the
ball hurled towards my sweaty face.
I kind of closed my eyes and put my
hands up in an attempt to both catch
the ball and shield my

face and when the ball never came

to me, I opened my eyes and saw

the ball slowly floating towards me.

Everything went into slow motion.

Except for me.

Chapter 13

It was the weirdest thing. With everything slowed down, I was able to not only dodge the incoming ball, but was also able to catch the one directly behind it as well as throw one at the opposing team.

"See, I told you I could be helpful!" said Lexi.

I smiled at her and she smiled back and then the game resumed in normal time.

I was getting people out one after another after another until it was

two on two. It was two of my best friends, Jack and Davis vs Lexi and me. It was on.

Lexi handed me the first ball and I threw it at Jack. It landed in his hands at first, but the impact of the throw was so powerful that it bounced out of his hands and onto the floor. One down, one to go.

Now it was time to end this.

Now look. I knew Davis. He was a smart, strategic thinker and all of his moves thus far were perfectly thought out and planned before they were put into action. I knew he was not going to just try and throw balls at me to get me out. He was going to do something annoyingly methodical.

Holding on to my one ball and staring down Davis who had two, I knew I had to do something other than just stand there. So I ran up to the line and Lexi shouts "throw it at his shoulder" and I did a fake out throw and then chucked it right at his chest instead. He quickly deflected it with the ball in his hand which left me with nothing. No ball, no protection.

However, I had something that he did not. I still had Lexi who turned out to be pretty awesome at dodgeball so it was not over yet.

I ran back to the base line and prepared for his next move. Davis then took a few steps forward and hurled a ball straight up into the air. I thought to myself, "That's it. I just won. I am going to catch this and he'll be out!" as I waited for the ball to fall into my hands.

Lexi yelled "Allie no!!!"

and ran to me and pulled me over just enough so that I was able to both catch the ball, and dodge the incoming one. Davis was out. "We won!!! I can't believe we actually won" I yelled to Lexi.

"That was so fun!! Let's do it again!"

Chapter 14

"Wow thanks Lexi, you really pulled through for me back there. That was EPIC"

"Yeah, of course Allie. Who knew we would be such a good team when it comes to sports? Oh wait...I did...hehehe"

"So cool. So with dyslexia, am I just really good at sports?"

"Well lets just say that I see things that most people can't and I will

always show you those things, which means that you will be able to see things that most people can't!"
"Sick! Thanks Lexi"

Now that gym was over, Lexi and I walked to my next class which was art with Mrs. Sherman. Mrs. Sherman was one of my favorite teachers because she was always so encouraging in class. Also she smelled like fresh biscuits everyday which made me like her more. I had her last year for art and really loved it.

We all sit down around two rectangular tables with a blank sheet of paper and some pencils in front of us. Mrs. Sherman then said "today we are going to draw this vase of flowers" and pulls out a vase of sunflowers and places it in the middle of the two tables.

Lexi then leans over and says to me "Aw yeah! I love drawing!! I can help you with this too!"

Excited at the prospect of Lexi and I working together again like we did in gym, I grabbed my pencil and said "Okay. What first?"

"Just start! I'll chime in when I see something"

So I started by looking at the three-dimensional object and began putting lines on the paper until it resembled the outline of

the vase and flowers in front of
me.

I showed Lexi and she said "that
looks like a nice start! Now make it
look more real by adding shading
here, here, here...."

and she grabbed my pencil and started shading for me.

With Lexi there, I knew exactly what I needed to do to make it look realistic. She helped me move faster so I was not hung up on little details but instead was able to complete a drawing by looking at it more holistically.

And it worked so well!

Mrs. Sherman was making her way around the room offering artistic advice to each kid she passed. Then as she walked by me,

she stopped for a second and asked
if she could show my picture to the
class. I reluctantly said yes, as I
was a little embarrassed to have
my work on display for everyone
to see.

"Class. Look at Allie's drawing! Do
you see the way she used shading to
make the vase really pop off the
page? Also take a look

at her composition. I love the way that she centered the flowers and the vase! I want everyone to try and focus on this for the next drawing" then she placed it down in front of me and said "really fantastic job Allie."

"Yay!! Good job Allie!" exclaimed Lexi.

"Couldn't have done it without you Lexi so thanks for the help" "Always. I wish I could help you with all your academics the way I am able to help you in sports and art"

"We can work on it. I'm sure there's a way to make us work" I hope so...

Chapter 15

After seeing how much Lexi helped me in gym and art, I was determined to find a way for us to work together in my other classes. "Lexi, lets make a game plan for academics. We are a great team in dodgeball and art so let's find a way to work like that in my academics"

"But I thought I wasn't helping you in your academics"

"Well maybe we can find a different way for you to help me that we both like"

"Okay well I really like art and color"

"Hmm..."

"Well I might have an idea" Lexi said timidly.

"What's that?"

"Well maybe you can write your notes in color so they are more like art and less like notes! I would like them more for sure"

"Ok perfect! I can do that. Any other ideas?"

"Hmmm...maybe well I also like music...so..." and she stood there for a while pondering ideas then said with excitement "Oh! For math and spelling with all those ugly equations and words you have to memorize, maybe we can make a song that looks neater in your brain! It would make me want to erase stuff a whole lot less and you can still memorize it all"

"I like that idea! That also sounds like more fun for me. Lets try them out and see how we feel."
"Alrighty!"

That week we put our ideas into action and tested them out along with a few other things. Some were better than others to say the least.

For example in Reading, I wrote down a few words on a piece of paper and let Lexi play with the words while I read. The goal was that I would be able to read and Lexi would be able to play. Since she would be playing, she wouldn't need to distract me. That didn't go too well. When she ran out of words to play with on the paper I gave her, she jumped right onto the page that I was reading out loud and started playing with those letters so I was reading gibberish to the class.

We tried a similar thing in math. Also did not work. But one class, while I was reading, I did everything I could to read exactly what was on the page. I read really slowly, kept my finger on the word I was reading and even

re-read a few words to make sure

Lexi didn't accidently switch them

and it worked!

Although Lexi continued to make

mistakes while trying to help me

which did mess me up, I could deal

with it. I just had to read a little

slower which was possible even

though it was annoying.

When it came to comprehension, I

still had problems remembering

what I had read. No question. But

I learned that if I re-read everything a few times over, I would eventually gain an understanding of what was on the page.

When it came to math I learned that Lexi really does not like clutter and because of this, would continue to erase the math equations I had memorized from my brain so I decided to start doing problems out the long way when I couldn't remember the answer.

Even though most of my friends had the answers memorized, I would continue working diligently until I arrived at an answer.

That worked pretty well even though it took a long time. Bottom line is that Lexi was manageable. Yes she made things harder for me, but what she did never stopped me. It just pushed me to work harder. It was actually nice getting to know and understand Lexi. Knowing that Lexi was the reason I was making mistakes and not doing well in math and reading was actually really nice to know. It meant that I wasn't ever bad at it. I just had Lexi there making it more challenging for me and that is why my answers are wrong.

Chapter 16

Now that I understand what Lexi is
and what she does, I have actually
come to like school a whole lot
more. Math is now one of my
favorite subjects even though it
takes me a while to do the
problems. I don't feel as
discouraged when I get the wrong
answer now because I know most
of the time it is just Lexi trying to
play. I now know that I am good

at math and apparently always have been.

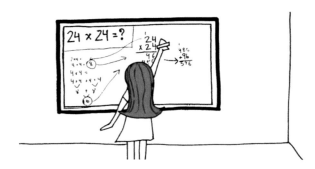

Basically what I have learned is a few things. One, Lexi is not going anywhere. She is here to stay whether I like it or not. Two, she is not evil. Although she makes some things harder for me, she always has good intentions and tries to help me. It's just sometimes it works, and other times it totally backfires and messes me up. Three, I need her. With her, I feel like I have super powers. I can literally do things that other people cannot do, see things that other people cannot see, and be someone no one else can be. Because of her I am creative, talented, and above all, a hard worker because I can't just do everything the easy way. She makes me work 10 times harder in my academics to get to the same place where my friends are but you know what? I don't care. I like it. Because of her I am me, and I wouldn't trade her for the world. Lexi is my best friend and she will always be by my side.

Thanks for all that you do Lex <3

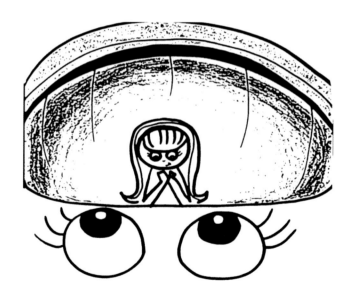

AUTHOR'S NOTE:

* * * * * * * * * * * * * * * * * *

My name is Aliah Banchik and I am a senior in high school. I have a special relationship with my dyslexia that I want to share. If you are reading this with dyslexia, I want you to know that you  are not alone. I want you to know you have a gift. Although some may argue the opposite, I am here to tell you you are brilliant, creative, resilient and so much more. Do not compare yourselves to your classmates as everyone has different strengths and you have many, so do not fear if you find that academics is not yours. You will find yours with the help of the guiding hand of your very own Lexi. Trust her to help you find your passion because she is an advantage. How so? Check out the next page for reasons why.

XO, Aliah

DYSLEXIA: What is it?

A different way of thinking.

- o A non-dyslexic brain uses parts of the brain that a dyslexic brain does not use while understanding text, numbers, etc.
- o Because of this, it may take longer for a dyslexic person to comprehend or read a passage or complete a math problem as it tries to decode what is in front of them with the only one part of the brain rather than three.
- o The Science: While reading, a non-dyslexic brain will use

three primary areas of the brain to break down the information in front of it (Broca's area, Parietal-temporal Area, Occipital-temporal Area). The dyslexic brain however, tends to rely on the Broca's area solely to do the functions of all three areas. Because only one area is being utilized, it is going to take longer for the brain to process and break down the information. Additionally, since the brain is not using the specialized areas, the product of will be less precise which is why we dyslexics tend to make mistakes as we read and flip things around.

o Studies have shown that dyslexic thinkers are more holistic thinkers than people without it. They may miss details that non-dyslexic brains may pick up, but overall, dyslexic brains will be able to understand the bigger picture while others are focused on the small details. This is one reason that so many dyslexic people are amazing artists, astrophysicists, and doctors.

o Among many other things, dyslexics tend to be very visual. They have very strong visual perceptual skills and are creative and

innovative thinkers
- Studies have shown that dyslexic people tend to have very strong reflexes and are able to respond to occurrences seen from their peripherals faster than non-dyslexics. One reason why dyslexic people are so good at sports.

FAMOUS PEOPLE WITH DYSLEXIA

★ **David Bois (Lawyer)**
★ Matthew H. Schneps (Astrophysicist)
★ Carole Greider (Scientist & Nobel Peace Prize Winner)
★ Whoopi Goldberg (Actor)
★ Steven Spielberg (Director)
★ Tim Tebow (Football Player)
★ Anderson Cooper (CNN News Anchor)
★ Jamie Oliver (Chef)
★ Cher (Singer)
★ Tom Cruise (Actor)
★ Tommy Hilfiger (Fashion Designer)
★ Muhammad Ali (Boxer)
★ Steve Jobs (Founder of Apple)
★ George Washington (First American President)
★ Leonardo Da Vinci (Artist)
★ Me!
★ My mom

SO MANY MORE

THANK YOUs

Thank you to all the people who without which I could not have created this book.

Thank you, Paul, for saving my Common App essay that one night and giving me the idea of personifying my dyslexia into Lexi for my college essay. This whole journey all started with you.

Thank you to my Great Aunt LaCrasia, for giving me the idea to turn my essay into a children's book.

Thank you to Riverdale Country School and the Senior Project committee for giving me the opportunity to explore this idea and create something powerful.

Thank you, Mr. Jason Ruff, for keeping me calm and laughing throughout the whole process of writing this book and for teaching me how to use Adobe Photoshop to bring my illustrations to life.

Thank you, Ms. Candy Anderson, for your unwavering support and encouragement from day one. Without you, I truly would not have the book I now have today. Thank you for your book recommendations, your wisdom, for sharing your personal stories with me regarding your experience with dyslexia around you, and for overall passion and knowledge for helping people. You are truly amazing.

Thank you, Nana, for constantly reminding me to do my best and to work hard for what I want. You kept me motivated and focused during this process and I love you so much!

Thank you, mom and dad, for your love and support throughout my entire journey with dyslexia. You guys have been there for me every step of the way and have supported me in ways I can't even explain. You both are a constant reminder that hard work and resilience pays off. You are my inspiration and my motivation, and I love you guys so much!

My Best Friend Lexi

My super power

44241585R00074

Made in the USA
Lexington, KY
09 July 2019